# BRU⟨ COCKBURN

## COMPLETE RECORDINGS ILLUSTRATED

## MIKE CURTIS & ANDREW SPARKE

Essential Discographies No.90

APS Books,
The Stables, Field Lane
Aberford,West Yorkshire,
LS25 3AE

APS Books is a subsidiary of the APS Publications imprint

**www.andrewsparke.com**

Cover photographs courtesy of Janet Spinas Dancer

# BRUCE COCKBURN

Bruce Cockburn should be as well-known and recognised globally as his fellow Canadian musicians Leonard Cohen, Joni Mitchell, Gordon Lightfoot, Robbie Robertson and Neil Young. Despite a 50 year career writing and singing powerful and tender songs about love, politics, human rights, religion and environmental issues, he seems to remain a secret for Canada where he has sold more than a million records.

In his song *Anthem*, Leonard Cohen sang: `There is a crack in everything, That`s how the light gets in`. Bruce Cockburn, in his song *Lovers in a Dangerous Time*, has the line `You gotta kick at the darkness `til it bleeds daylight`. In the song *God Part II*, U2`s Bono sings about `hearing a singer on the radio late last night, says he`s gonna kick at the darkness `til it bleeds daylight`. Bruce Cockburn is given an honourable mention in the Rattle and Hum album credits.

Cockburn seems to have been kicking at the door to wider fame throughout his career – not that he ever been troubled by it. He released his first solo album in 1970 and had his first minor hit outside Canada nine years later. This was *Wondering Where The Lions Are* from his ninth album `Dancing in the Dragon`s Jaws` - it reached 21 on the US Billboard 100 and got him a slot on NBC`s Saturday Night Live television programme. There have been more than 30 studio and live albums across his career.

Where does a newcomer to Bruce Cockburn start? I would go for `The Charity of Night`, released in 1997. Love, travel, politics, serious, witty..... The album opens with that rollicking sound, rolling back and forth as the train rattles on through the night....`and the rhythm of the night train is a mantra`. Bruce will offer you the anti-landmine song up against the one of the most sensual love songs you will ever hear (*Live on my Mind*). There is reflection and frustration at daily life in `Pacing The Cage`. Powerful, rip roaring electric guitar contrasts against the finest acoustic pickings. There are vibes from the class jazzman Gary Burton and backup vocals from Bonnie Raitt, Maria Muldaur, Ani Difranco and The Grateful Dead`s Bob Weir. The second track *Get Up Jonah* opens with the line: `Woke up thinking about Turkish drummers, didn't take long, don't know much about Turkish drummers`.

The following album, `Breakfast in New Orleans, Dinner in Timbuktu`, opens with the line `Slid out of my dreams like a baby out of the nurse`s hands, onto the hard floor of day`. It is another fine album with a broad swath of songs and instrumentals including a cover of `Blueberry Hill`. Another opens with the line `Judge says to the hooker, can you come out to play? I`ve been condemning people all day long, that`s how I get paid`.

Two other earlier albums are good entry points for someone discovering Bruce Cockburn. `Humans` (1980) includes the song *Rumours of Glory* which Bruce used as the title of his well-received autobiography published in 2014 and the accompanying compilation box set of eight cds and one concert dvd. The box set had 116 tracks including 15 previously unreleased.

The `Stealing Fire` album (1984) opens with the thumping bass line of `Lovers in a Dangerous Time`, one of his most powerful songs which has been covered by several artists including the Canadian band Bare Naked Ladies – or BNL as Cockburn prefers to reference them. Other artists who have covered Cockburn`s songs include Jimmy Buffet, Judy Collins, k.d.lang, Chet Atkins and the Jerry Garcia Band,

The songs on `Stealing Fire` came out of a visit to Nicaragua in 1983 on behalf of the Canadian branch of Oxfam. Cockburn was moved by the plight of refugees and his lyrics highlighted life in the third world. His frustration at the conditions and the ongoing warfare was spelt out in *If I Had a Rocket Launcher* although he denied it was a call to arms but simply `a cry`. The song made the US Billboard 100 and a video got extensive air play on MTV. Throughout his career, Cockburn has highlighted human rights and has worked with, not just Oxfam, but also with Amnesty International, Doctors without Borders, and Friends of the Earth.

He became a Christian early in his career and his 1970s albums often reflected his faith at the time. In his autobiography, he wrote: `Along the way I found Jesus Christ, then let go of his hand amid the din of disingenuous right-wing Christian exploitation. I have attempted to live my life somewhat in line with his Word, without necessarily taking it as, well, gospel`. He says faith and grace still frequently find a place in his lyrics.

In later years, he supported the campaigns against land mines and the deforestation of the Amazon. Apart from Central America, Cockburn`s activism has also taken him to Nepal, Iraq and Afghanistan, when his brother was serving there in 2009 as a medical officer with the Canadian forces.

Cockburn has been inducted into the Canadian Music Hall of Fame and the Order of Canada, and he has been awarded more than a dozen Juno Awards (Canadian equivalent of the Grammys) as well as the Allan Slaight Humanitarian Spirit Award.

Bruce Cockburn was born in 1945 in Ottawa, which explains why the lyrics and credits on many of his album covers are in French as well as English. Some 20 years later he was busking in Paris before returning to Canada to play in several bands, one of which opened for both Cream and Jimi Hendrix. His first solo appearance was at the Mariposa Folk Festival in 1967. Over the years he has performed solo and with small bands.

Apart from his song writing capabilities, Cockburn is also recognised as a very fine guitarist on both electric and acoustic guitar. He has released two instrumental albums - `Speechless` and `Crowing Ignites`. His style and skill become particularly apparent on the concert albums such as `Circles in the Stream` and `Slice O Life`. You can find a video on-line of Cockburn on stage in Montreal in 1988 with David Crosby, Stephen Stills and Graham Nash. Stills introduces him warmly and Nash tells the audience `they should be very proud` of their fellow Canadian. All three watch in wonder as Cockburn`s fingers float up and down the fretboard.

Jackson Browne is an admirer. Writing about Cockburn`s autobiography, he said: `This is the story of the development of one of the most astute and compelling songwriters in the English language. Rumours of Glory is a highly personal account, by one whose quest for expression engages the most important social questions of our time`.

Official website: http://brucecockburn.com

The Cockburn Project: https://cockburnproject.net/

*The Cockburn Project is a unique website that exists to document the work of Canadian singer-songwriter and musician Bruce Cockburn. The central focus of the Project is the ongoing archiving of Cockburn's self-commentary on his songs, albums and issues. You will also find news, tour dates, an on-line store and other current information.*

Gavin`s Woodpile – Bruce Cockburn on-line newsletter:

https://www.brucecockburn.org/

# ALBUMS

## BRUCE COCKBURN
### *(1970 True North Records)*

Going To The Country
Thoughts On A Rainy Afternoon
Together Alone
The Bicycle Trip
The Thirteenth Mountain
Musical Friends
Change Your Mind
Man Of A Thousand Faces
Spring Song
Keep It Open

*Dennis Pendrith: Bass*

# HIGH WINDS WHITE SKY
### *(1971 True North Records)*

Happy Good Morning Blues
Let Us Go Laughing
Love Song
One Day I Walk
Golden Serpent Blues
High Winds White Sky
You Point To The Sky
Life's Mistress
Ting/The Cauldron
Shining Mountain
*2003 Rounder Records reissue bonus tracks*
Totem Pole*(live)*
It's An Elephant's World*(live)*

*Eugene Martynec-Second Guitar*
*Eric Nagler-Mandoline Banjo, Mandolin*
*Michael Craydon-Marimba, Tables, Tree Bell, Boobams, Pygmy Rhythm Log*
*John Wyre-Cymbals, Gongs, Salad Bowls*

## SUNWHEEL DANCE
### *(1971 True North Records)*

My Lady And My Lord
Feet Fall On The Road
Fall
Sunwheel Dance
Up On The Hillside
Life Will Open
It's Going Down Slow
When The Sun Falls
He Came From The Mountain
Dialogue With the Devil (or 'Why don't we celebrate')
For The Birds
*2005 Rounder Records reissue bonus tracks:*
Morning Hymn
My Lady And My Lord*(solo)*

*Trisha Cullen, accordian*
*Ian Guenther, violin*
*Carol Marshall, cello*
*Eugene Martynec - electric guitar, piano and electronics*
*Eric Nagler - jaw harp*
*Dennis Pendrith - bass*
*John Savage - drums*

# NIGHT VISION
*(1973 True North Records)*

Foxglove
You Don't Have To Play The Horses
The Blues Got The World
Mama Just Wants To Barrelhouse All Night Long
Islands In A Black Sky
Clocks Don't Bring Tomorrow, Knives Don't Bring Good News
When The Sun Goes Nova
Deja Vu
Lightstorm
God Bless The Children

*Pat Godfrey-Keyboards*
*Dennis Pendrith-Bass*
*John Savage-Percussion*

## SALT, SUN AND TIME
### *(1974 True North Records)*

All The Diamonds
Salt, Sun And Time
Don't Have To Tell You Why
Stained Glass
Roulersa Bosse ("To Knock About the World")
Never So Free
Seeds On The Wind
It Won't Be Long
Christmas Song

*Eugene Martynec: guitar and synthesizer*
*Jack Zaza: clarinet*

# JOY WILL FIND A WAY
## *(1975 True North Records)*

Hand-dancing
January In The Halifax Airport Lounge
Starwheel
Lament For The Last Days
Joy Will Find A Way (A Song About Dying)
Burn
Skylarking
A Long-time Love Song
A Life Story
Arrows Of Light

*Dennis Pendrith-Bass*
*Terry Clarke-Drums*
*Dido Morris-Percussion*
*Pat Godfrey-Keyboards*
*Eugene Martynec-Guitar*
*Tommy Graham Tambora*
*Beverley Glenn-Copeland-Background Vocals*

## IN THE FALLING DARK
### *(1976 True North Records)*

Lord Of The Starfields
Vagabondage ('Drifting')
In The Falling Dark
Little Seahorse
Water Into Wine
Silver Wheels
Gift Bearer
Gavin's Woodpile
I'm Gonna Fly Someday
Festival Of Friends
*2002 Rounder Records reissue bonus tracks*
Red Brother Red Sister
Untitled Guitar
Shepherds
Dweller By A Dark Stream

*Michael Donato: bass*
*Bob Disalle: drums*
*Bill Usher: percussion*
*Kathryn Moses: flutes, piccolo*
*Jørn Anderson: percussion*
*Dennis Pendrith: bass*
*Fred Stone: fluegelhorn, trumpet*
*Luke Gibson, Lyn MacDonald & Erin Malone: background vocals*

# CIRCLES IN THE STREAM
### *(1977 True North Records)*

The Pipes, The Pipes
Starwheel
Never So Free
Deer Dancing Round A Broken Mirror)
Homme Brûlant ('Burning Man')
Free To Be
Mama Just Want to Barrelhouse All Night Long

| | |
|---|---|
| Cader Idris | Lord of the Starfields |
| Arrows of Light | All the Diamonds |
| One Day I Walk | Dialogue With The Devil |
| Love Song | Joy Will Find a Way |
| Red Brother Red Sister | God Bless the Children |

*2005 Rounder Records reissue bonus track*
Deer Dancing Round A Broken Mirror

*Robert Boucher: bass*
*Pat Godfrey: electric piano, marimbas and vocals*
*Doug Mackay: bagpipes*
*Bill Usher: percussion and voice*

*Recorded live at Massey Hall, Toronto 8th-9th April, 1977*

# FURTHER ADVENTURES OF BRUCE COCKBURN
### *(1978 True North Records)*

Rainfall
A Montreal Song
Outside A Broken Phone Booth With Money In My Hand
Prenons La Mer ('Let Us Take To The Sea')
Red Ships Take Off In The Distance
Laughter
Bright Sky
Feast Of Fools
Can I Go With You
Nanzen Ji
*2002 Rounder Records reissue bonus track*
Mountain Call

*Bob DiSalle: drums and percussion*
*Eugene Martynec: electric guitar*
*Kathryn Moses: flute*
*Martha Nagler: bodhran*

# DANCING IN THE DRAGON'S JAWS
### *(1979 True North Records)*

Creation Dream
Hills Of Morning
Badlands Flashback
Northern Lights
After The Rain
Wondering Where The Lions Are
Incandescent Blue
No Footprints
*2002 Rounder records reissue bonus tracks*
Dawn Music
Bye Bye Idi

*Pat Godfrey: Piano and Marimba,*
*Robert Boucher: Bass*
*Bob DiSalle: Drums*

## IIUMANS
## (1980 True North Records)

Grim Travellers
Rumours Of Glory
More Not More
You Get Bigger As You Go
What About The Bond
How I Spent My Fall Vacation
Guerrilla Betrayed
Tokyo
Fascist Architecture
The Rose Above The Sky
*2003 reissue bonus track*
Grim Travellers *(live)*

*Dennis Pendrith: Bass*
*Jon Goldsmith: Keyboards*
*Hugh Marsh: Violin*
*Patricia Cullen: Synthesizer*
*Pat LaBarbera: Reeds*
*Bob DiSalle: Drums*
*Kathy Moses, Beverly Glen-Copeland, Rachel Paiement: Vocals*

## RESUMÉ
### *(1981 Millennium)*

Silver Wheels
The Coldest Night Of The Year *(previously unissued)*
Can I Go With You
Laughter
Water Into Wine
Mama Just Wants To Barrelhouse All Night Long
Lord Of The Starfields
Outside A Broken Phone Booth With Money In My Hand
Dialogue With The Devil

*Compilation including one previously unissued track*

## MUMMY DUST
### *(1981 True North Records)*

Silver Wheels
Loner
Joy Will Find A Way
Thoughts on a Rainy Afternoon
It's Going Down Slow
The Coldest Night Of The Year *(previously unreleased)*
Laughter
Red Brother Red Sister
You Don't Have to Play the Horses
Dweller By A Dark Stream *(previously unreleased)*
All the Diamonds in the World

*Compilation including one previously unissued track*

# INNER CITY FRONT
## *(1981 True North Records)*

You Pay Your Money And You Take Your Chance
The Strong One
All's Quiet On The Inner City Front
Radio Shoes
Wanna Go Walking
And We Dance
Justice
Broken Wheel
Loner
*2002 Rounder records reissue bonus tracks*
The Coldest Night Of The Year
The Light Goes On Forever

*Memo Acevedo: Percussion*
*Bob DiSalle: Drums*
*Dennis Pendrith: Bass guitar*
*Jon Goldsmith: Keyboards*
*Hugh Marsh: Violin and Mandolin*
*Kathryn Moses: Reeds and Background Vocals*

# THE TROUBLE WITH NORMAL
## *(1983 True North Records)*

The Trouble With Normal
Candy Man's Gone
Hoop Dancer
Waiting For The Moon
Tropic Moon
Going Up Against Chaos
Put Our Hearts Together
Civilizations And It`s Discontents
Planet Of The Clowns
*2002 Rounder Records release bónus tracks*
Cala Luna
I Wanna Dance With You

*Bob DiSalle: Drums*
*Jon Goldsmith: Keyboards*
*Hugh Marsh: Violin and mandolin*
*Dennis Pendrith: Bass and stick*
*Dick Smith: Percussion*

## STEALING FIRE
### *(1984 True North Records)*

Lovers In A Dangerous Time
Maybe The Poet
Sahara Gold
Peggy's Kitchen Wall
To Raise The Morning Star
Nicaragua
If I Had A Rocket Launcher
Dust And Diesel
*2003 reissue bonus tracks:*
Yanqui Go Home
Call It The Sundance

*Jon Goldsmith – keyboards*
*Fergus Marsh – bass and stick*
*Miche Pouliot – drums*
*Chi Sharpe – percussion*

## RUMOURS OF GLORY
### *(1985 Plane Records)*

The Trouble With Normal
Going Up Against Chaos
Wondering Where The Lions Are
Tokyo
All's Quiet On The Inner City Front
Creation Dream
Wanna Go Walking
Grim Travellers
Rumours Of Glory
Tropic Moon
Yanqui Go Home
Lord Of The Starfields
The Coldest Night Of The Year
Laughter
The Rose Above The Sky

*German compilation*

## WORLD OF WONDERS
### *(1986 True North Records)*

Call It Democracy
Lily Of The Midnight Sky
World Of Wonders
Berlin Tonight
People See Through You
See How I Miss You
Santiago Dawn
Dancing In Paradise
Down Here Tonight

*Jon Goldsmith: keyboarads*
*Fergus Jemison Marsh: bass and stick*
*Hugh Marsh: violin*
*Chi Sharpe: percussion*
*Michael Sloski: drums*
*Michael Alan White: trumpet, flugelhorn and conch*
*Judy Cade: background vocals*

# WAITING FOR A MIRACLE
## (Singles 1970-1987)
### *(1987 True North Records)*

Going to the Country
Musical Friends*
One Day I Walk
It's Going Down Slow
Up on the Hillside*
Feet Fall on the Road*
Mama Just Wants to Barrelhouse All Night Long (from the film
'Rumours of Glory')
All the Diamonds
Burn
Silver Wheels
I'm Gonna Fly Someday*
Vagabondage*
Free to Be*
Laughter
Wondering Where the Lions Are
Tokyo
Fascist Architecture
The Trouble with Normal

Rumours of Glory
The Coldest Night of the Year
Wanna Go Walking*
You Pay Your Money and you Take Your Chance
Tropic Moon*
Candy Man's Gone*
Lovers in a Dangerous Time
If I Had a Rocket Launcher
Making Contact*
Peggy's Kitchen Wall
People See Through You
Call it Democracy
See How I Miss You*
*New songs*
Stolen Land
Waiting For A Miracle

*Bonus tracks on Canadian CD compilation*

## BIG CIRCUMSTANCE
### *(1988 True North Records)*

If A Tree Falls
Shipwrecked At The Stable Door
Gospel Of Bondage
Don't Feel Your Touch
Tibetan Side Of Town
Understanding Nothing
Where The Death Squad Lives
Radium Rain
Pangs Of Love
The Gift
Anything Can Happen
If A Tree Falls *(acoustic version)*

*Jon Goldsmith – keyboards and electric auto harp*
*Fergus James Marsh – stick and bass*
*Michael Sloski – drums and percussion*
*Background vocals: Judy Cade, Margaret O'Hara and Mose Scarlett*
*Hugh Marsh – violin*
*Myron Schultz – clarinets*

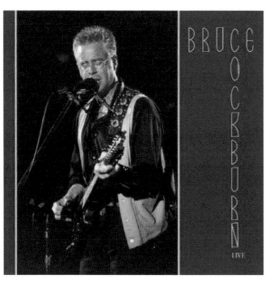

# LIVE
## *(1990 True North Records)*

Silver Wheels
World of Wonders
Rumours of Glory
See How I Miss You
After the Rain
Call It Democracy
Tibetan Side of Town
Wondering Where The Lions Are
Nicaragua
Broken Wheel
Stolen Land
To Raise The Morning Star
Maybe the Poet
Always Look On The Bright Side Of Life
*2002 Rounder Records reissue bonus track:*
If I Had A Rocket Launcher

*Recorded live at Ontario Place, Toronto, 14th and 15ᵗʰ August 1989*

*Fergus Jemison Marsh: Chapman stick, midi stick and background vocals*
*Michael Sloski: drums, percussion and background vocals*

## NOTHING BUT A BURNING LIGHT
### *(1991 True North records)*

A Dream Like Mine
Kit Carson
Mighty Trucks Of Midnight
Soul Of A Man
Great Big Love
One Of The Best Ones
Somebody Touched Me
Cry Of A Tiny Babe
Actions Speak Louder
Indian Wars
When It's Gone, It's Gone
Child Of The Wind

## CHRISTMAS
### *(1993 True North Records)*

Adeste Fidelis
Early On One Christmas Morn
O Little Town Of Bethlehem
Riu Riu Chiu (Nightingale's Sounds)
I Saw Three Ships
Down In Yon Forest
Les Anges Dans Nos Campagnes (The Angels In Our Midst)
Go Tell It On The Mountain
Shepherds
Silent Night
Iesus Ahatonnia/The Huron Carol
God Rest Ye Merry Gentlemen
It Came Upon The Midnight Clear
Mary Had A Baby
Joy To The World

## DART TO THE HEART
### *(1994 True North Records)*

Listen For The Laugh
All The Ways I Want You
Bone In My Ear
Burden Of The Angel/Beast
Scanning These Crowds
Southland Of The Heart
Train In The Rain
Someone I Used To Love
Love Loves You Too
Sunrise On The Mississippi
Closer To The Light
Tie Me At The Crossroads

# THE CHARITY OF NIGHT
## *(1997 True North Records)*

Night Train
Get Up Jonah
Pacing The Cage
Mistress Of Storms
The Whole Night Sky
The Coming Rains
Birmingham Shadows
The Mines Of Mozambique
Live On My Mind
The Charity Of Night
Strange Waters

*Guest musicians include Gary Burton, Gary Craig, and Rob Wasserman, plus special guests Jonatha Brooke, Ani DiFranco, Patty Larkin, Maria Muldaur, Bonnie Raitt and Bob Weir.*

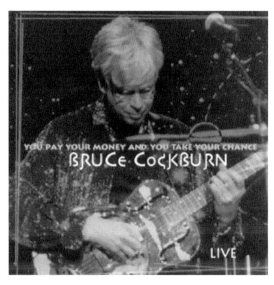

# YOU PAY YOUR MONEY AND
# YOU TAKE YOUR CHANCE
### *(1998 True North Records)*

Call It Democracy
Stolen Land
Strange Waters
Fascist Architecture
You Pay Your Money And You Take Your Chance
Birmingham Shadows

*Recorded live at the Barrymore Theater, Madison, Wisconsin on 3rd May 1997.*

*Bass and background vocals: Steve Lucas*
*Drums and background vocals: Ben Riley*

## BREAKFAST IN NEW ORLEANS
## DINNER IN TIMBUKTU
### *(1999 True North Records)*

When You Give It Away
Mango
Last Night Of The World
Isn't That What Friends Are For?
Down To The Delta
The Embers Of Eden
Blueberry Hill
Let The Bad Air Out
Look How Far
Deep Lake
Use Me While You Can

*Features special guest appearances by Margo Timmins (Cowboy Junkies) and Lucinda Williams, and performances from Daniel Janke on the West African kora, and Richard Bell on keyboards.*

# ANYTHING ANYTIME ANYWHERE
## THE SINGLES 1979-2002
### *(2002 True North Records)*

My Beat *(new song)*
Wondering Where The Lions Are
Tokyo
The Coldest Night Of The Year *(remix)*
The Trouble With Normal
Lovers In A Dangerous Time
If I Had A Rocket Launcher
Call It Democracy
Waiting For A Miracle *(remix)*
If A Tree Falls
A Dream Like Mine
Listen For The Laugh
Night Train
Pacing The Cage
Last Night of the World
Anything Anytime Anywhere *(new song)*

# YOU'VE NEVER SEEN EVERYTHING
## *(2003 True North Records)*

Tried And Tested
2. Open
3. All Our Dark Tomorrows
4. Trickle Down
5. Everywhere Dance
6. Put It In Your Heart
7. Postcards From Cambodia
8. Wait No More
9. Celestial Horses
10. You've Never Seen Everything
11. Don't Forget About Delight
12. Messenger Wind

*Guest vocalists include Emmylou Harris, Sarah Harmer, Jackson Browne and Sam Phillips.*

# SPEECHLESS
## *(2005 True North Records)*

Foxglove
Train In The Rain
Water into Wine
Elegy
Mistress Of Storms
Rouler Sa Bosse
Salt, Sun and Time
Islands In A Black Sky
Rise And Fall
Sunrise On The Mississippi
King Kong Goes To Tallahassee
When It's Gone It's Gone
Deep Lake
End Of All Rivers
Sunwheel Dance

*Instrumental album*

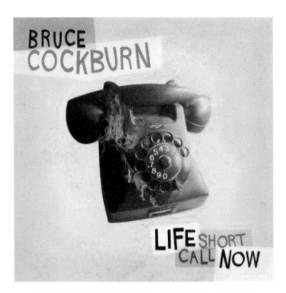

## LIFE SHORT CALL NOW
### *(2006 True North Records)*

Life Short Call Now
See You Tomorrow
Mystery
Beautiful Creatures
Peace March
Slow Down Fast
Tell The Universe
This Is Baghdad
Jerusalem Poker
Different When It Comes To You
To Fit In My Heart
Nude Descending A Staircase

*Gary Craig: Drums and Percussion*
*David Piltch: Acoustic and Electric Bass*
*Julie Wolf: Piano, Harmonium, Wurlitzer, Fender Rhodes, Accordion and*
*Melodica*
*Jonathan Goldsmith: Celeste, Glockenspiel, Maikotron, Keyboards*
*Kevin Turcotte: Flugelhorn and Trumpet*

# SLICE O LIFE
### *(2009 True North Records)*

World Of Wonders
Lovers In A Dangerous Time
Mercenary Story
See You Tomorrow
Last Night Of The World
How I Spent My Fall Vacation
Tibetan Side of Town
Pacing The Cage
Bearded Folk Singer Story
End Of All Rivers

Soul Of A Man
Wait No More
City Is Hungry
Put It In Your Heart
Tramps In The Street Story
If A Tree Falls
Celestial Horses
If I Had A Rocket Launcher
Child Of The Wind
Tie Me At The Crossroads

*Soundcheck*
String Thing *including* The Trains Don't Run Here Anymore
Kit Carson
Mama Just Wants To Barrelhouse All Night Long

*Recorded live early 2008 at series of 9 concerts in the North Eastern United States and 1 in Quebec*

## SMALL SOURCE OF COMFORT
### *(2011 True North Records)*

The Iris Of The World
Call Me Rose
Bohemian 3-Step
Radiance
Five Fifty-One
Driving Away
Lois On The Autobahn
Boundless
Called Me Back
Comets Of Kandahar
Each One Lost
Parnassus and Fog
Ancestors
Gifts

## RUMOURS OF GLORY
## BOX SET
### *(2014 True North Records)*

*8CD box set plus DVD of Bruce Cockburn Live – The Slice O Life Tour film*

The Charity Of Night
If A Tree Falls
Man Of A Thousand Faces
One Day I Walk
Let Us Go Laughing
Bird Without Wings
Thoughts On A Rainy
Afternoon
Sunwheel Dance
Foxglove
Going To The Country
It's An Elephant World
You Don't Have To Play The
Horses
Creation Dream
Shining Mountain
15. Hills Of Morning
16. Change Your Mind
17. He Came From The
Mountain
18. Musical Friends

Fall
Blues Got The World
Mama Just Wants To
Barrelhouse All Night Long
All The Diamonds In the World
Rouler Sa Bosse
Don't Have To Tell You Why
Red Brother Red Sister
Gavin's Woodpile
Stolen Land
Lord Of The Starfields
Silver Wheels
Little Sea Horse
Celestial Horses
Feast Of Fools
Can I Go With You
Wondering Where The Lions
Are
Incandescent Blue
How I Spent My Fall Vacation
What About The Bond

Fascist Architecture
Rumours Of Glory
You Pay Your Money And You
Take Your Chance
All's Quiet On The Inner City
Front
Justice
Broken Wheel
The Trouble With Normal
Tropic Moon
If I Had A Rocket Launcher
Waiting For A Miracle
Dust & Diesel
Yanqui Go Home
Nicaragua
Peggy's Kitchen Wall
Santiago Dawn
Maybe The Poet
Lover's In A Dangerous Time
To Raise The Morning Star
People See Through You
Planet Of The Clowns
Berlin Tonight
Where The Death Squad Lives
Anything Can Happen
Call It Democracy
Gospel Of Bondage
Shipwrecked At The Stable
Door
Radium Rain
Understanding Nothing
Tibetan Side Of Town
Child Of The Wind
Great Big Love
One Of The Best Ones

Soul of A Man
Cry Of A Tiny Babe
Kit Carson
Indian Wars
A Dream Like Mine
Someone I Used To Love
All The Ways I Want You
Live On My Mind
Bone In My Ear
Listen For The Laugh
The Mines Of Mozambique
The Coming Rains
Pacing The Cage
Night Train
The Whole Night Sky
Strange Waters
The Embers Of Eden
Get Up Jonah
When You Give It Away
Mango
Last Night Of The World
Use Me While You Can
Put It In Your Heart
All Our Dark Tomorrows
Trickle Down
Postcards From Cambodia
You've Never Seen Everything
My Beat
Tried And Tested
Tell The Universe
This Is Baghdad
9. Mystery
10. Beautiful Creatures
11. The Light Goes On Forever

## RARE AND PREVIOUSLY UNRELEASED
Juan Carlos Theme
Waterwalker
My Hometown Avalon
Wise Users
Going Down The Road

The Whole Night Sky
Grinning Moon
Song For Touring Around The Stars
Come Down Healing
Mystery Walk
The Trains Don't Run Here Anymore
Ribbon Of Darkness
Turn Turn Turn
Honey Babe Let The Deal Go Down

## DVD LIVE – THE SLICEO LIFE TOUR

*Recorded 15th to 17th May 2008 live at The Iron Horse, Northhampton, MA, the Somerville Theatre, Boston, MA and the Kulp Auditorium, Ithaca, NY*

Lovers In A Dangerous Time
How I Spent My Fall Vacation
Last Night of The World
If I Had A Rocket Launcher
Tibetan Side Of Town
The End Of All Rivers
Going To The Country
Pacing The Cage
This Is Baghdad
Stolen Land
King Kong Goes To Tallahassee
Child Of The Wind
If A Tree Falls
Wondering Where The Lions Are
Mystery
Put It In Your Heart
World Of Wonders
Wait No More

## BONE ON BONE
### *(2017 True North Records)*

States I'm In
Stab At Matter
Forty Years In The Wilderness
Cafe Society
3 Al Purdys*
Looking And Waiting
Bone On Bone
Mon Chemin (My Road)
False River
Jesus Train
Twelve Gates To The City

## CROWING IGNITES
### *(2019 True North Records)*

Bardo Rush
Easter
April In Memphis
Blind Willie
Seven Daggers
The Mt. LeFroy Waltz
Sweetness And Light
Angels In The Half Light
The Groan
Pibroch: The Wind In The Valley
Bells Of Gethsemane

*Instrumental album*

## FOUR NEW SONGS
### *(2021 True North Records)*

*These songs were released on YouTube to help raise money for the San Francisco Lighthouse Church to support its work, which includes support for homeless people in San Francisco, and for Lighthouse Kathmandu, a Nepali-run organization dedicated to fighting human trafficking.*

On A Roll
Orders
When You Arrive
Us All

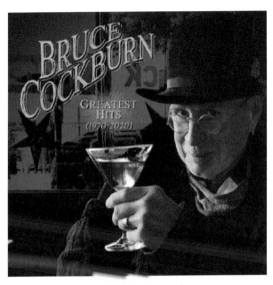

## GREATEST HITS 1970-2021
### *(2021 True North Records)*

.Going to the Country
Musical Friends*
One Day I Walk
Mama Just Wants to
Barrelhouse All Night Long
All the Diamonds
Silver Wheels
Wondering Where the Lions
Are
Tokyo
Rumours of Glory
The Coldest Night of the Year
Wanna Go Walking
The Trouble With Normal
Lovers in a Dangerous Time
If I Had a Rocket Launcher
Call It Democracy

People See Through You
Waiting For A Miracle
Stolen Land
If A Tree Falls
A Dream Like Mine
Listen For The Laugh
Night Train
Pacing The Cage
Last Night of the World
Anything, Anytime, Anywhere
Open
Put It In Your Heart
Different When It Comes To
You
Call Me Rose
States I'm In

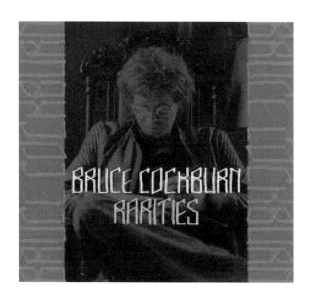

## RARITIES
### *(2022 True North Records)*

Juan Carlos Theme
Waterwalker Theme
Avalon, My Home Town
Wise Users
Going Down The Road
The Whole Night Sky (Alternate Version)
Grinning Moon
Song For Touring Around The Stars
Come Down Healing
Mystery Walk
The Trains Don't Run Here Anymore (Re-Mastered)
Ribbon Of Darkness (Re-Mastered)
Turn, Turn, Turn (Re-Mastered)
Honey Babe Let The Deal Go Down (Re-Mastered)
Twilight on the Champlain Sea (feat. Ani DiFranco)
Bird Without Wings

*(The Rarities disc from the box set Rumours of Glory plus
two additional tracks)*

# SINGLES

Going To The Country/Thoughts On A Rainy Afternoon *1970*
Musical Friends/Keep It Open *1970*
One Day I Walk/High Winds White Sky *1971*
It's Going Down Slow/Morning Hymn *1972*
Up On The Hillside/Feet Fell On The Road *1972*
Burn/Burn *(mono)* *1975*
Mama Just Wants To Barrelhouse All Night Long/When The Sun Goes Nova *1973*
Burn/Burn (mono) *1975*
I'm Gonna Fly Some Day/Giftbearer *1976*
Free To Be/Deer Dancing Round A Broken Mirror *1977*
Laughter/Prenons La Mer *1978*
Wondering Where The Lions Are/Rainfall *1979*
Tokyo/Incandescent Blue *1980*
Rumours Of Glory/You Get Bigger As You Go *1981*
I'm Okay (Fascist Architecture)/How I Spent My Fall Vacation *1981*
Radio Shoes/Broken Wheel *1981*
You Pay Your Money and You Take Your Chance/The Light Goes On Forever *1982*
Wanna Go Walking/Radio Shoes *1981*
And We Dance/Justice/Coldest Night Of The Year *1981*
Coldest Night Of The Year/Joy Will Find A Way *1981*
The Trouble With Normal/Cala Luna *1982*
Waiting For The Moon/The Trouble With Normal *1983*
Candy Man's Gone/Civilization And Its Discontents *1983*
Tropic Moon/Candy Man's Gone *1983*
Lovers In A Dangerous Time/Nicaragua *1984*
Lovers In A Dangerous Time/Sahara Gold *1984*
Making Contact/Nicaragua *1984*
If I Had A Rocket Launcher/Maybe The Poet *1984*
Peggy's Kitchen Wall/To Raise The Morning Star 1984
Call It Democracy/Dancing In Paradise 1985
People See Through You/Santiago Dawn 1985

See How I Miss You/Berlin Tonight *1986*
Waiting For A Miracle/Vagabondage *1987*
Stolen Land/One Day I Walk *1987*
If A Tree Falls/The Gift *1988*
Where The Death Squad Lives/Don't Feel Your Touch *1988*
Don't Feel Your Touch/Understanding Nothing *1989*
Shipwrecked At The Stable Door/Anything Can Happen *1989*
Silver Wheels/Silver Wheels *1990*
A Dream Like Mine/When It's Gone, It's Gone *1991*
Great Big Love/Great Big Love *(rock mix) 1992*
Somebody Touched Me/Somebody Touched Me *(version) 1992*
Listen For The Laugh/Burden Of Angel-Beast/Southland Of The Heart/Tie Me At The Crossroads *1994*
Burden Of Angel-Beast/Scanning These Crowds/If I Had A Rocket Launcher *1994*
Southland Of The Heart *1994*
Closer To The Light *1994*
Someone I Used To Love *1995*
Night Train *1997*
The Whole Night Sky/The Coming Rains/Mistress Of The Storms *1997*
Pacing The Cage/Pacing The Cage *(live acoustic)*/Night Train *(live acoustic) 1997*
Last Night Of The World *1999*
When You Give It Away *1999*
My Beat *2002*
Open/Tried And Tested/Put It In Your Heart *2003*
Different When It Comes To You/Life Short Call Now/This Is Baghdad *2006*

# DVDS

# FURTHER READING

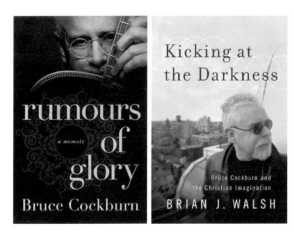

Printed in Great Britain
by Amazon